MENTAL HEALTH AND ME

First published in Great Britain in 2023 by Hodder & Stoughton

Editor: Julia Bird
Art director and layout: Salvador Maldonado
Character designer: Eleonor Hunter
Background design: Faith-Maria Ijelu, Philip Askins, Maxime Dupuy, Laura Bartlett, Rachel Trebicki & Salvador Maldonado.

With thanks to Evie O' Sullivan, Emma Austin and Emma White at MIND

HB ISBN: 978 1 4451 7115 9
PB ISBN: 978 1 4451 7116 6
Printed in India

MIX
Paper from
responsible sources
FSC® C104740

Franklin Watts
An imprint of
Hachette Children's Group
Part of Hodder and Stoughton
Carmelite House
50 Victoria Embankment
London EC4Y 0DZ

An Hachette UK Company

www.hachette.co.uk
www.hachettechildrens.co.uk

PLEASE BE AWARE THAT THIS BOOK CONTAINS
SCENES AND DESCRIPTIONS THROUGHOUT
THAT MAY BE UPSETTING OR DISTURBING, AND
COULD POTENTIALLY ACT AS A TRIGGER. THESE
INCLUDE DESCRIPTIONS OF SELF-HARM AND
SUICIDAL THOUGHTS. PLEASE ONLY READ ON
IF YOU FEEL ABLE TO DO SO.

FOREWORD

'Mental Health and Me' is based on an animated series Mosaic Films made for the BBC. We interviewed young people who were experiencing difficulties with their mental health, and then combined these interviews with animation. By using real testimony, together with thoughtful and engaging animation, we felt that we were offering an accessible way to understand mental ill-health, in a way that people could either identify with themselves, or empathise with what others might be experiencing. What you see here is those interviews and illustrations, put into graphic novel form in a way that is equally – if not more – engaging and accessible. The stories here offer a glimpse into what it is like to deal with mental health problems on a daily basis; the struggles, the feelings of isolation and the hopelessness that sometimes ensue.

As a former clinical psychologist, and now a filmmaker and author, this project has been extremely close to my heart; for in our research, in which I spoke to young people, it saddened me to witness how so many seem to be struggling with psychological difficulties, sometimes without the full understanding of what was happening to them, or that all-important empathy from others around them. It's clear not enough is being done, in terms of increasing understanding, addressing issues of stigma and prejudice, and signposting the various forms of help and support that are indeed available on the journey to recovery. It is my hope that the experiences in this book can help form part of that journey.

CONTENTS

JACK

a story about anorexia

I WAS A NORMAL CHILD.

I WAS PLAYING FOOTBALL...

RUGBY...

CRICKET...

TENNIS...

ALL THE SPORTS UNDER THE SUN.

IF THERE WAS A BALL INVOLVED I WAS PRETTY MUCH THERE.

BUT THINGS CHANGED WHEN MY PARENTS SPLIT UP,
WHICH WAS WHEN I WAS 11 YEARS OLD.

AND THAT'S WHEN MY HEAD
STARTED TO QUESTION
THINGS THAT I WOULD NOT HAVE
QUESTIONED BEFORE.

I THOUGHT
IT WAS
MY FAULT.

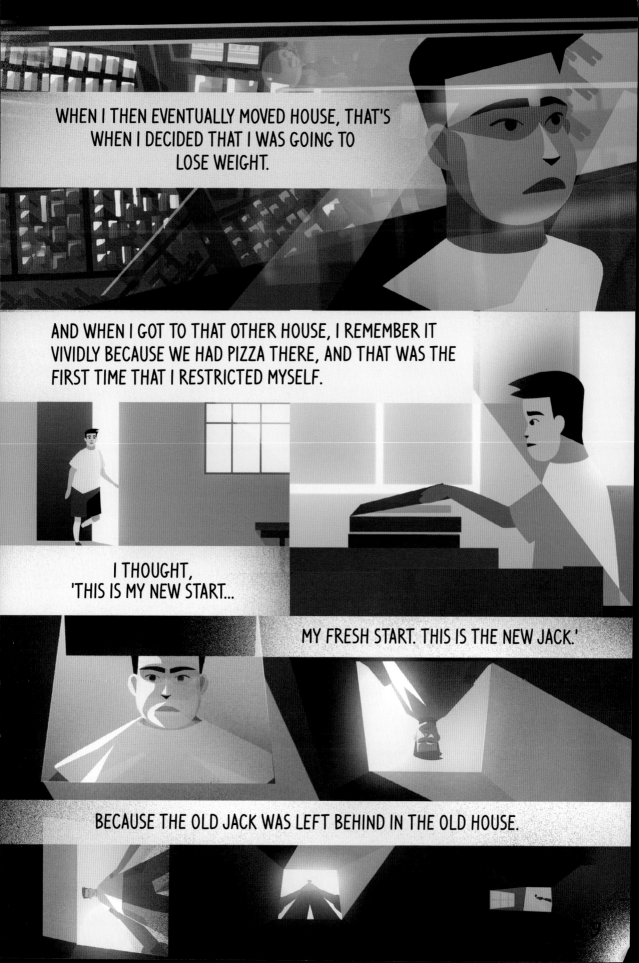

I STARTED RUNNING AND I REMEMBER MY ROAD WAS VERY LONG,
SO I JUST WENT UP ONCE AND THEN CAME BACK DOWN.

AND THEN I WENT SWIMMING.

SO ONE NIGHT – RAN UP ONCE, CAME DOWN, WENT TO SWIM.

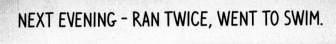

THEN PROBABLY A COUPLE OF DAYS PASSED - THREE TIMES, SWIM.

FOUR TIMES, SWIM.

FIVE TIMES, SWIM.

I JUST FELT SO DETERMINED.

NOTHING WAS GOING TO STOP ME.

I WAS GOING TO DO THIS.

I REMEMBER SAYING TO ONE OF MY MATES, WHEN I WAS WALKING OUT OF THE GATE AT SCHOOL...

"I AM GOING TO BE SKINNY JACK."

AND HE SAID:
"I CAN'T IMAGINE A SKINNY JACK."

I SAID:
"JUST WATCH ME."

MY RELATIONSHIP WITH FOOD AND EXERCISE —
I WENT WAY TOO FAR WITH IT.

I ISOLATED MYSELF FROM EVERYONE.

I REMEMBER GOING ON HOLIDAY TO SPAIN, AND THAT WAS A BIG WAKE-UP CALL FOR MY MUM. I THINK THAT WAS WHEN MY MUM REALISED THERE WAS SOMETHING SERIOUSLY WRONG.

I'D HAVE PANIC ATTACKS AFTER DINNER.
I WOULD HAVE THESE WEIRD MOOD SWINGS.

I WAS SO UNCOMFORTABLE IN MYSELF AND
WHAT I LOOKED LIKE AND HOW I FELT.

ANOREXIA IS LIKE A CLOUD FLOODING YOUR BRAIN.

YOU'RE JUST THINKING ABOUT NUMBERS, CALORIES, EXERCISE.

WHAT YOU ARE EATING TODAY, WHAT YOU ARE EATING TOMORROW.

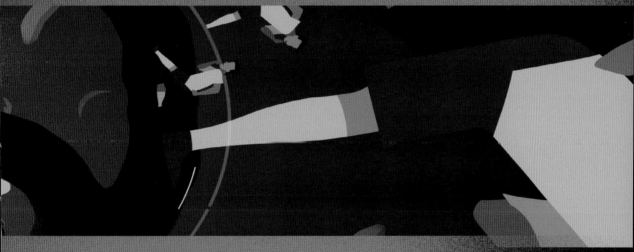

WHAT CAN YOU CUT OUT?
WHAT CAN YOU DO MORE TO PUSH YOURSELF?

I WASN'T PRESENT.

I WAS NOW 'SKINNY JACK'.
I HAD TURNED MYSELF INTO THAT PERSON.

I BECAME VERY WEAK. I JUST FELT EMPTY.

I COULDN'T EVEN RUN ANYMORE.

EVERYTHING HAD STOPPED AND I WAS IN BED BY SIX.

THERE WAS NO WAY I WAS UP ANY LATER,
BECAUSE I COULDN'T PHYSICALLY STAY UP.

I WAS SO TIRED AND DRAINED.

BY NOVEMBER, I WAS STRUGGLING TO WALK TO SCHOOL.

I USED TO GO STRAIGHT TO THE MEDICAL ROOM.

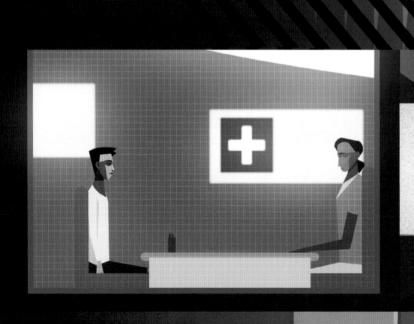

I'D TELL THEM TO CALL MY PARENTS TO PICK ME UP BECAUSE I COULDN'T WALK HOME.

AT THIS POINT I WANTED TO BE ILL. I WANTED TO FEEL BAD...

I WAS SO FAR GONE IN MY
HEAD THAT I WASN'T JACK.

I HAD TURNED INTO A COMPLETELY DIFFERENT PERSON.

AND I JUST WANTED TO BE
IN THAT BUBBLE, BY MYSELF.

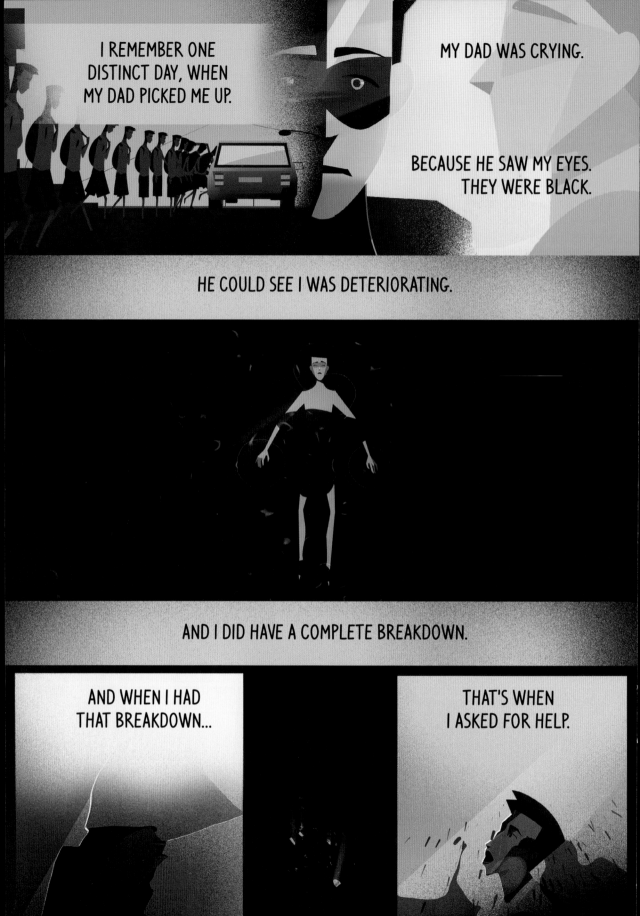

I REMEMBER ONE DISTINCT DAY, WHEN MY DAD PICKED ME UP.

MY DAD WAS CRYING.

BECAUSE HE SAW MY EYES. THEY WERE BLACK.

HE COULD SEE I WAS DETERIORATING.

AND I DID HAVE A COMPLETE BREAKDOWN.

AND WHEN I HAD THAT BREAKDOWN...

THAT'S WHEN I ASKED FOR HELP.

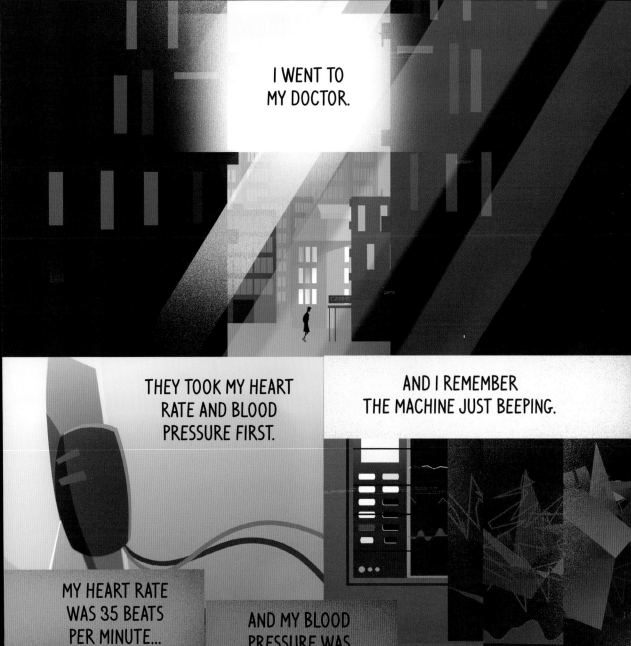

I WENT TO
MY DOCTOR.

THEY TOOK MY HEART
RATE AND BLOOD
PRESSURE FIRST.

AND I REMEMBER
THE MACHINE JUST BEEPING.

MY HEART RATE
WAS 35 BEATS
PER MINUTE...

AND MY BLOOD
PRESSURE WAS
70 OVER 40...

OR SOMETHING
INSANE.

I SAID: "AM I GOING TO DIE?"
AND THE DOCTOR SAID: "WE NEED TO GO AND SPEAK TO YOUR DAD."

THEY TOOK ME UP TO THE WARD UPSTAIRS.

I JUST REMEMBER LOOKING TO MY LEFT AND THERE WERE PEOPLE MY AGE, MAYBE A BIT YOUNGER AND OLDER...

AND THEY WERE BEING FED BY TUBES.

AND I REMEMBER JUST WALKING AND THINKING...

'I AM GOING TO START NOW. I HAVE TO DO THIS.'

AND THAT WAS THE DAY I STARTED MY WHOLE MEAL PLAN – ON THAT DAY.

THINGS STARTED TO LOOK UP BECAUSE I HAD STRUCTURE AGAIN. SO I'M STUDYING FOR EXAMS AND I'VE GOT MY MEAL PLAN.

I'M AN OUTPATIENT AT A MENTAL HEALTH UNIT. I'M GOING ONCE OR TWICE A WEEK, TO GET WEIGHED, MY HEART CHECKED, TO GET EVERYTHING CHECKED UP.

AND THAT'S THE THING, I TOOK CONTROL OF MY OWN RECOVERY. YOU HAVE TO HELP YOURSELF.

A COUNSELLOR OR PSYCHOLOGIST CAN ONLY BRING YOU TO WATER, THEY CAN'T MAKE YOU DRINK IT. YOU HAVE TO ACTUALLY WANT TO DO IT YOURSELF.

INDIA

a story about self harm

WHEN I FIRST STARTED AT SECONDARY SCHOOL...

IT WAS DAUNTING...

IT WAS EXCITING...

IT WAS SORT OF EVERY SINGLE EMOTION AT ONCE.

I THINK IT WAS SORT OF AN IDENTITY CRISIS.
I DIDN'T REALLY KNOW WHO I WAS, BUT I WANTED TO BE SOMEONE.

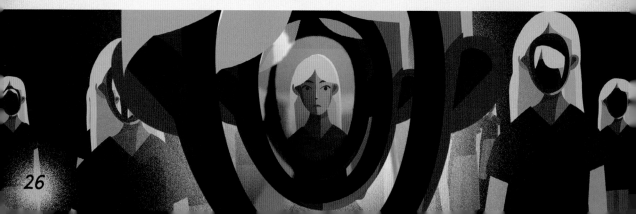

I HAD TO WEAR A CERTAIN TYPE OF CLOTHING,
I HAD TO LISTEN TO THE SAME MUSIC AS EVERYONE ELSE.

I CUT MY HAIR REALLY SHORT.

I HAD TO DO
THE SAME THINGS.

I THOUGHT I WOULDN'T CARE WHAT
OTHER PEOPLE THOUGHT.

PEOPLE USED TO TEASE ME ABOUT WHAT I LOOKED LIKE,
HOW I ACTED.

IT NIGGLED AWAY AT ME A LITTLE BIT...

AND THAT TINY LITTLE NIGGLING
MADE ME REALLY INSECURE.

I WASN'T HAPPY
WITH WHO I WAS.
I DIDN'T LIKE THE WAY I LOOKED.

I WAS WORRIED ABOUT HOW SMART I WAS.

I WAS WORRIED ABOUT MY FRIENDSHIPS.

I THOUGHT THEY'D SEE SOMEONE WHO WAS DIFFERENT, WHO WAS UGLY, WHO WAS NOT FRIENDSHIP-WORTHY.

I HAD EPISODES WHERE I'D GET REALLY, REALLY UPSET.
I DIDN'T KNOW HOW TO DEAL WITH IT.

SO I ENDED UP HIDING. I'D SPEND
A LOT OF TIME IN THE TOILETS.

IT WAS A SQUARE,
I WAS IN THE SQUARE,
NOTHING CAN HAPPEN
IN THE SQUARE.

IT WAS AN AREA
I COULD BE
IN CONTROL...

AS EVERYTHING ELSE FELT LIKE IT WAS A
MASSIVE CLUMP OF WORRIES LIKE...

'WHAT WILL HAPPEN ON THE SCHOOL BUS TONIGHT?'

OR 'DID ANYONE SEE ME EATING THAT AT LUNCH?'

OR 'OH NO, I JUST SAID THAT IN CLASS AND
DIDN'T MEAN TO AND PEOPLE ARE LAUGHING
AT ME NOW.'

I DIDN'T WANT
TO GO BACK OUT
THERE IN CASE
SOMETHING
HAPPENED.

THIS SCARED FEELING SORT OF BECAME UNCONTROLLABLE.

EVERYTHING WAS INTENSIFIED, SO LIGHTS WOULD BECOME LIGHTER...

DARKNESS WOULD BECOME DARKER, SOUNDS WOULD GET NOISIER...

THE TEACHER TALKING ON THE OTHER SIDE OF THE ROOM WAS SUDDENLY SCREAMING AT ME.

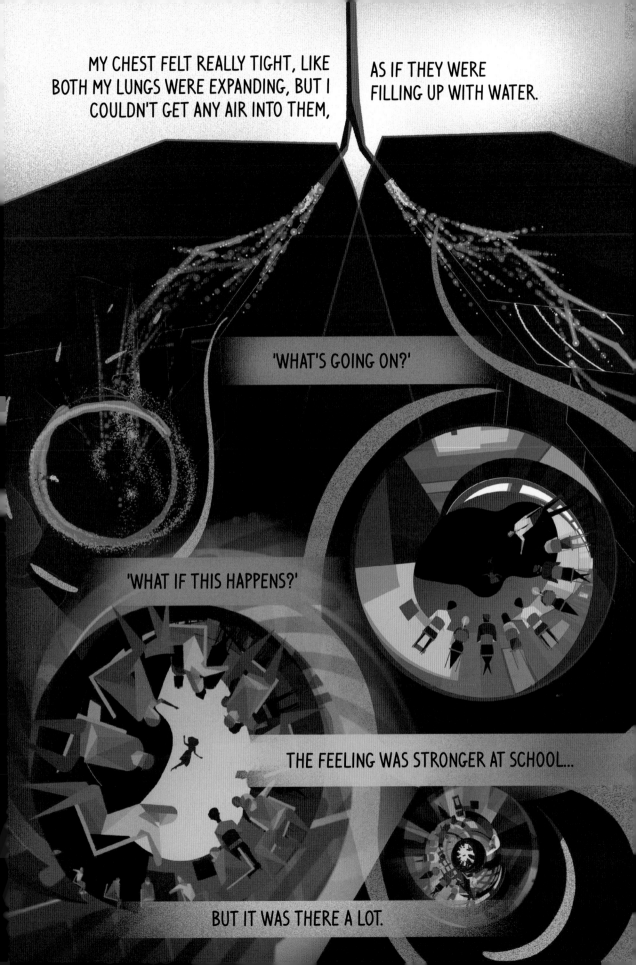

MY FRIEND, SHE WENT THROUGH A DIFFICULT TIME.

HER METHODS OF COPING ALMOST RUBBED OFF ON ME IN A WAY.

IN THE MIDDLE OF A FRENCH LESSON SHE SAID...

"WE NEED TO GO TO THE BATHROOM."
AND SO SHE LEFT AND
I LEFT FIVE MINUTES LATER.

SHE SAID: "INDIA I NEED TO TELL YOU THIS." AND SHE JUST LIFTED UP HER SLEEVES.

I SAID: "WHAT'S THAT?" AND SHE SAID: "THIS IS WHAT I DO TO MYSELF."

HER ARMS WERE CUT AND SCRATCHED AND BURNED AND PENNED AND EVERYTHING.

IT WAS LIKE A CRIME SCENE ON SKIN.

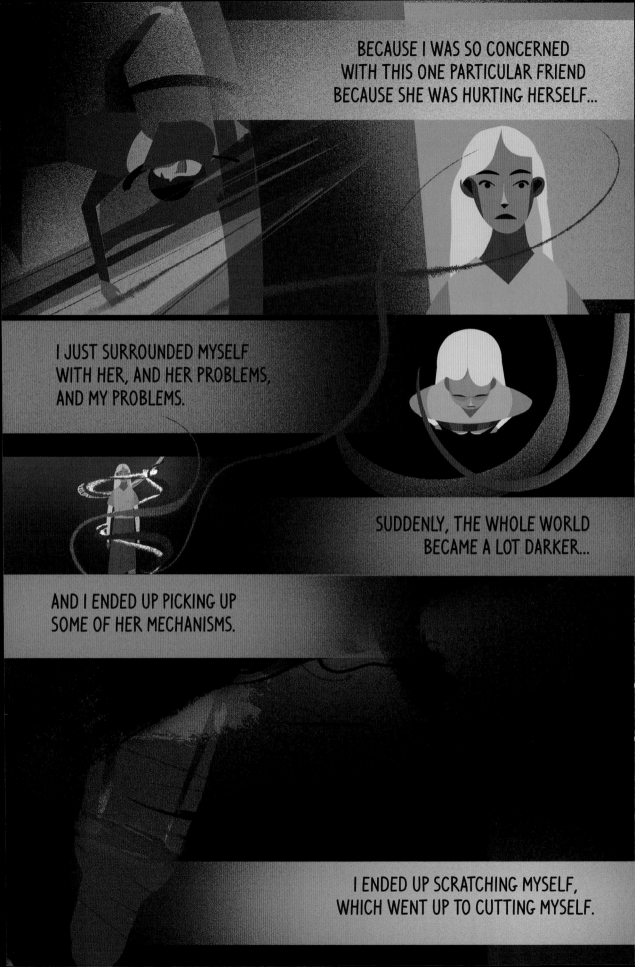

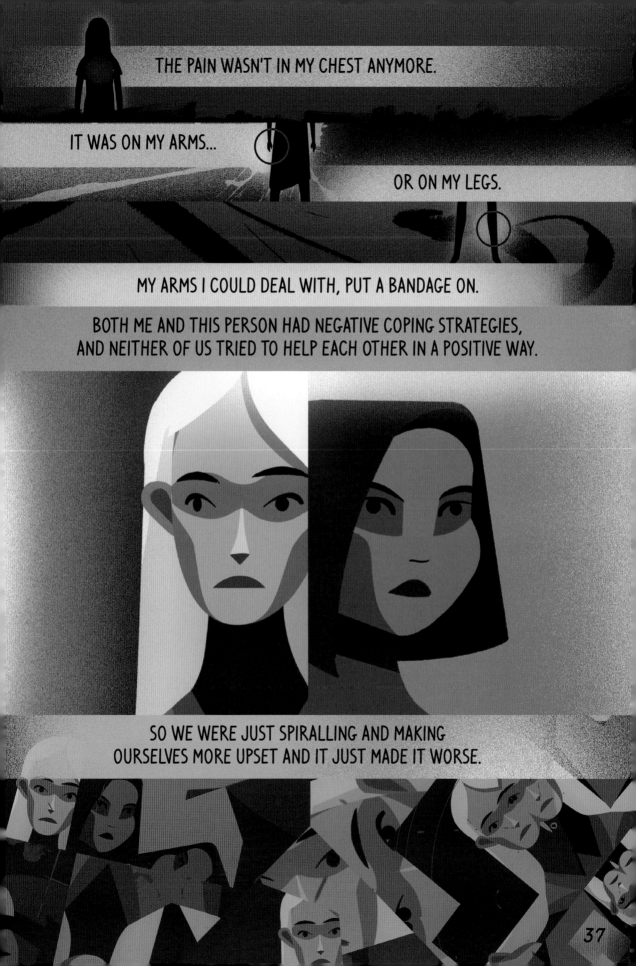

THE PAIN WASN'T IN MY CHEST ANYMORE.

IT WAS ON MY ARMS...

OR ON MY LEGS.

MY ARMS I COULD DEAL WITH, PUT A BANDAGE ON.

BOTH ME AND THIS PERSON HAD NEGATIVE COPING STRATEGIES, AND NEITHER OF US TRIED TO HELP EACH OTHER IN A POSITIVE WAY.

SO WE WERE JUST SPIRALLING AND MAKING OURSELVES MORE UPSET AND IT JUST MADE IT WORSE.

MY PARENTS FOUND OUT ABOUT MY SELF-HARM
ON MY MUM'S 40TH BIRTHDAY, WHICH WAS HORRENDOUS –
IT WAS JUST A VERY, VERY SAD DAY.

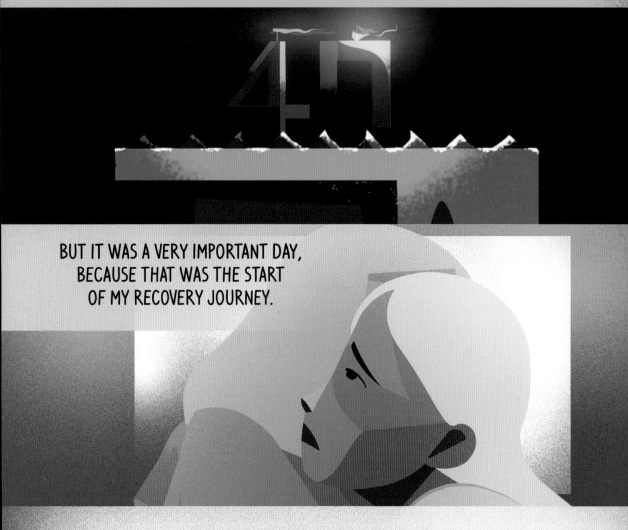

BUT IT WAS A VERY IMPORTANT DAY,
BECAUSE THAT WAS THE START
OF MY RECOVERY JOURNEY.

IF MY PARENTS HADN'T FOUND OUT,
I DON'T KNOW WHAT WOULD HAVE HAPPENED.

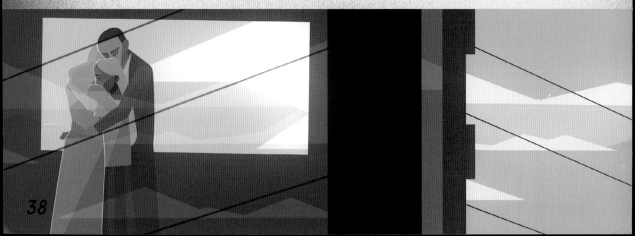

I WAS REFERRED BY MY DOCTOR TO A CHILD AND ADOLESCENT MENTAL HEALTH SERVICE. MY THERAPIST WAS A REALLY LOVELY PERSON WHOM I TRUSTED.

SHE TAUGHT ME HOW TO TALK TO PEOPLE WITHOUT WORRY AND THAT WAS REALLY IMPORTANT.

THE FACT THAT I COULD NOW TALK TO PEOPLE MEANT THAT I DIDN'T HAVE TO HIDE AWAY.

I'VE ALMOST COMPLETELY STOPPED SELF-HARMING.
I'M DEALING WITH IT A LOT BETTER AND I'M GETTING STRONGER,
THOUGH I DON'T THINK IT'S EVER GOING TO GO AWAY.

MY RELATIONSHIPS WITH PEOPLE ARE BETTER
AND I CAN BE MUCH MORE SOCIAL.
I'M A HAPPIER PERSON,
BECAUSE I KNOW HOW TO DEAL
WITH THINGS IN A POSITIVE WAY.

NOW THAT I KNOW HOW TO
HELP MYSELF, I CAN ALSO HELP
OTHER PEOPLE, AND THAT
MAKES ME FEEL GOOD.
I LIKE HELPING OTHER PEOPLE.

CHLOE

a story about addiction

FROM THE LITTLE BITS THAT I CAN REMEMBER
FROM WHEN I WAS YOUNGER,
IT WAS GOOD AND
I HAD A PRETTY TIGHT FAMILY.

I WAS PRETTY NAIVE TO EVERYTHING.

WE ALL LIVED ON THE SAME STREET, GOT ON WITH ALL OUR NEIGHBOURS.

I WAS SEEING MY DAD EVERY WEEKEND WITH MY BROTHER.

THEN MUM TOOK IN WHO WAS TO BE HER NEW BOYFRIEND.
HE DIDN'T HAVE A LOT GOING FOR HIM, BUT IT WAS MAINLY HIS KIDS WHO WERE THE ISSUE.

THE OLDER ONE WOULD DO ANYTHING TO GET ME IN TROUBLE. SHE'D BREAK THINGS, SHE'D STEAL THINGS.

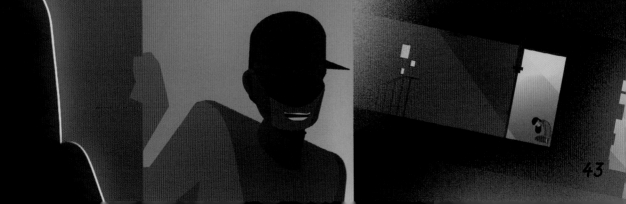

THEN THE YOUNGER ONE, HE WAS JUST A HORRIBLE PERSON.

FROM WHAT I CAN REMEMBER, THAT'S WHEN IT ALL STARTED GOING DOWNHILL.

MY MUM GOT A DRUG HABIT, MAINLY BROUGHT ON
BY HER NEW BOYFRIEND. SHE STARTED TO GO OFF THE RAILS A BIT.

HE WAS HAVING A BIG INFLUENCE ON HER.
THEY WOULD TAKE US OUT TO PARTIES TIL 3 A.M. ON A SUNDAY.

I DON'T KNOW IF IT WAS A NEW YEAR'S PARTY OR A BIRTHDAY PARTY,
BUT WE WERE JUST TOLD TO GO OFF AND PLAY.
JUST GO AND PLAY OUTSIDE OR WHATEVER...

AND I CAME TO FIND MUM — AND I SAW HER PASSED OUT OVER A COOKER.

I JUST REMEMBER SCREAMING AND
EVERYONE TELLING ME TO GET OUT.

MUM WOULDN'T GET UP IN THE MORNINGS
TO TAKE US TO SCHOOL. WE WERE HAVING TO GET
OURSELVES UP, MAKE OUR OWN LUNCH.

MY BROTHER'S GOT AUTISM AND DURING MUM'S 'PHASE',
HE STARTED GETTING BIGGER AND ANGRIER.
SO HE WAS TAKEN OUT OF THE SITUATION BY THE REST OF MY FAMILY.

HE COULDN'T CONTROL
THE AGGRESSION.
THAT HAD A BIG IMPACT,
BECAUSE ALL MY CONFIDENCE
FROM THEN ON JUST DISAPPEARED.

I STARTED SEEING MY DAD A LOT LESS AS WELL,
WHICH WAS REALLY DIFFICULT.

I STARTED SMOKING A BIT OF WEED RECREATIONALLY, AND THEN I STARTED FINDING IT REALLY HELPED MY MOOD.

I WASN'T FEELING THE EXTREMES THAT I NORMALLY FELT. I COULD ACTUALLY GET THROUGH THE DAY AND GET OUTSIDE.

IT WAS LITERALLY LIKE MY AIR. I COULDN'T DO ANYTHING WITHOUT IT.

AND THEN FROM THAT I STARTED TO KNOW PEOPLE.

I GUESS I SORT OF GOT MYSELF INTO THE WRONG CROWD,
AND IT WASN'T JUST WEED – THEN CAME THE ECSTASY.

I'D NEVER FELT
HAPPINESS LIKE IT.
IT WAS THE BEST
FEELING IN THE WORLD.

THE ONLY THING
I COULD LOOK FORWARD TO
WAS THE NEXT TIME
I WAS GETTING
OFF MY FACE.

AND THEN CAME THE COCAINE. THAT'S PROBABLY BEEN THE WORST,
JUST BECAUSE OF HOW DIFFICULT IT HAS BEEN TO COME OFF IT.

TO BREAK THE HABITS, TO LEARN THAT LITTLE BIT OF SELF CONTROL.

I COULDN'T GO OUT
FOR A WEEKEND,
I COULDN'T GO AND STAY AT
A FRIEND'S HOUSE,
BECAUSE I WOULDN'T BE
ABLE TO SMOKE
AND THAT WAS MY PRIORITY.

THAT WAS PROBABLY THE WORST THING ABOUT IT,
THE FACT THAT IT SORT OF TOOK OVER MY LIFE.

IT WAS A CASE OF GOING INTO SCHOOL STONED
AND THEN BY THE END OF THE DAY...

I'M EXHAUSTED...   I'M GRUMPY...   I'M AGITATED.

I GUESS IT ALL JUST GOT TOO MUCH.
I WAS FEELING SUICIDAL.
I TOLD MY MUM STRAIGHT AWAY.

I WENT TO HOSPITAL AND THAT'S
WHEN I WAS BASICALLY TOLD:
"IF YOU WANT THE HELP
AND YOU WANT TO GET BETTER,
YOU HAVE TO STOP OTHERWISE
YOU'RE NOT GONNA GET IT."

I STARTED TO GET
IN TOUCH WITH MYSELF MORE,
STARTED TO UNDERSTAND
THE WAY I WAS FEELING,
AND I STARTED TALKING
ABOUT HOW I WAS FEELING.

IT'S VERY EARLY DAYS,
BUT I FEEL A LOT MORE FREE NOW.
I HAVE THE ABILITY TO TALK
ABOUT THINGS.

I HAVEN'T TOUCHED COCAINE IN QUITE A WHILE...

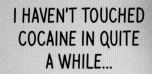

I HAVEN'T TOUCHED ECSTASY.

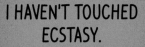

BUT THE HARDEST PART HAS BEEN STOPPING SMOKING.

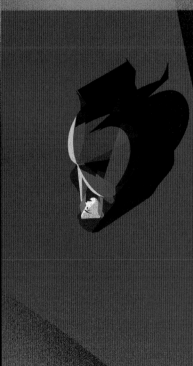

IT WAS JUST ABOUT BREAKING THOSE BARRIERS. THE FIRST DAY – I WOULDN'T BE ABLE TO SLEEP, I WOULDN'T BE ABLE TO EAT, BUT THEN THE NEXT DAY I SORT OF FELT ALIVE.

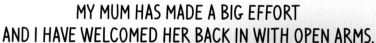

MY MUM HAS MADE A BIG EFFORT
AND I HAVE WELCOMED HER BACK IN WITH OPEN ARMS.

SHE IS THE ONLY REAL FAMILY I HAVE,
AND I KNOW HER CHILDHOOD WASN'T EASY.

NOW SHE KNOWS THE MISTAKES SHE'S MADE.
I KNOW SHE FEELS GUILTY
AND SHE'S LIVING THROUGH THIS AS WELL.

RYAN

a story about bullying

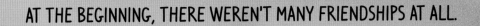

AT THE BEGINNING, THERE WEREN'T MANY FRIENDSHIPS AT ALL.

AS PRIMARY SCHOOL DEVELOPED, THERE WERE A FEW,
BUT THEY WEREN'T SUSTAINABLE.

PEOPLE THOUGHT THEY'D BECOME BETTER BY HANGING
AROUND WITH A SO-CALLED 'POPULAR PERSON'.

IT WAS ALL 'WHO IS THE COOLEST?'
AND 'WHO IS THE MOST POPULAR?'

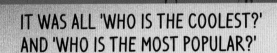

AND I WAS ALWAYS THE OPPOSITE OF THAT.

THE SMALLEST
THINGS STARTED.
JUST KIND OF
NAME-CALLING.

THE USUAL WORDS...
THE 'N' WORD.

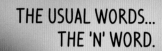

THEN THAT ESCALATED - PEOPLE WOULD PICK UP ROCKS
AND THROW THEM OR AIM THEM AT MY HEAD WHILE
REPEATEDLY USING DEROGATORY WORDS.

ONE OF THE 'POPULAR
PEOPLE', SO TO SPEAK,
HE USED ONE OF THE
KNIVES FROM
THE CANTEEN.

HE KEPT PRODDING
ME WITH IT,
HOPING TO
INTIMIDATE ME.

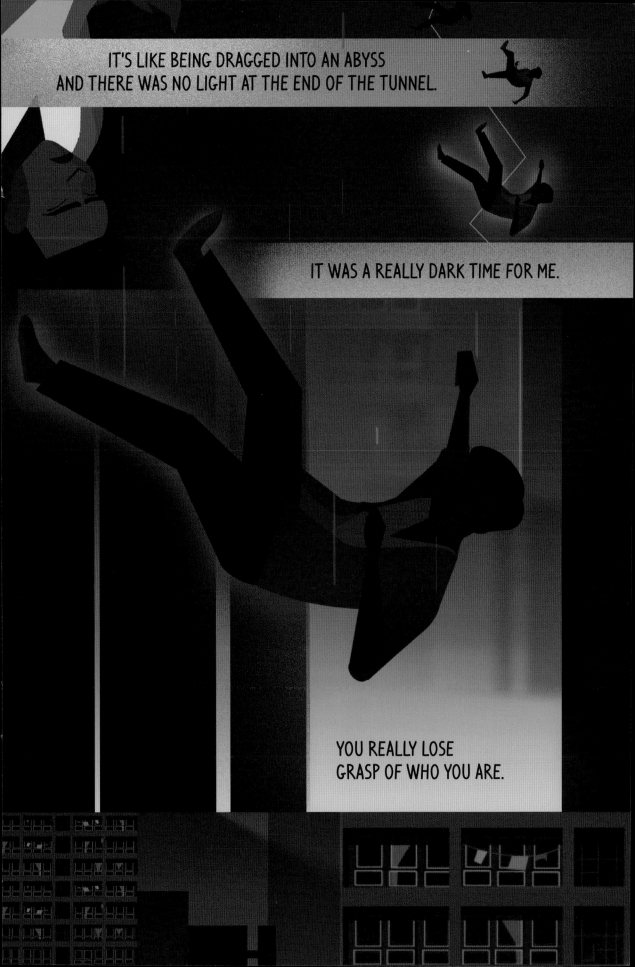

WHEN YOU COME HOME FROM SCHOOL AND YOU ARE BROKEN,
YOU WANT SOME ENCOURAGEMENT...

OR JUST A SLIVER OF HOPE FROM PEOPLE WHO
ARE MEANT TO BE YOUR FAMILY.

SO TO BE CONSTANTLY DEGRADED AT HOME TOO...

IT WAS BECOMING MORE AND MORE LIKE A ONE-WAY STREET.

AND THERE WAS ONLY ONE WAY THAT WAS HEADING,
WHICH WAS THE PERMANENT SOLUTION AND THE WORST SOLUTION.

SCHOOL BECAME
AN ESCAPE FROM HOME...

AND HOME BECAME
AN ESCAPE FROM SCHOOL.

I DEVELOPED AN ALTER EGO WHO SPOKE
DIFFERENTLY, WHO PORTRAYED HIMSELF DIFFERENTLY.

I'D PRETEND THAT MY UPBRINGING
WAS THE ABSOLUTE OPPOSITE OF WHAT IT REALLY WAS.

I'D PRETEND THAT I HAD A LOT OF MONEY
AND THAT I CAME FROM A REALLY PRIVILEGED BACKGROUND.

IT DIDN'T GIVE ME POSITIVE ATTENTION,
BUT IT DID GIVE ME ATTENTION.

AT THIS POINT, ANY ATTENTION WAS BETTER THAN FEELING
THAT YOU ARE JUST LOCKED AWAY IN A DRAWER.

THERE WAS NOTHING IN THAT SUIT ANYMORE,
IT WAS JUST A CHARACTER – A COMPLETE THEATRICAL MASK.

IN THE MORNINGS,
I WOULD PHYSICALLY VOMIT
AT THE THOUGHT OF
WHO I WAS BECOMING.

IT RESULTED IN ME REFUSING TO GO TO SCHOOL,
WHICH GRADUALLY AMPLIFIED.

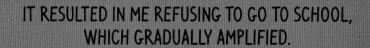

IT REACHED THE POINT WHERE I WOULDN'T LEAVE MY ROOM.
I WOULDN'T RESPOND AT ALL.

AND AT THIS POINT,
TWO-AND-A-HALF YEARS INTO SECONDARY SCHOOL...

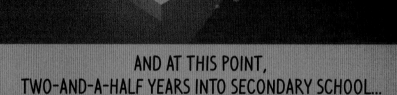

THE JENGA TOWER COLLAPSED.
I HAD FALLEN INTO MYSELF.

IT WAS THE WORST TIME IN MY LIFE.
I WOULDN'T ALLOW ANY LIGHT INTO THE HOUSE.

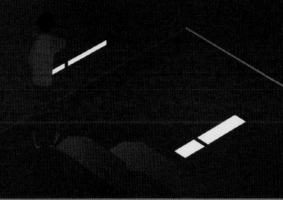

I'D BE HUDDLED IN THE FETAL POSITION.

I HAD NO FORM OF CONTACT THROUGH THE DAY,
AND I'D CRY THROUGH THE NIGHT.

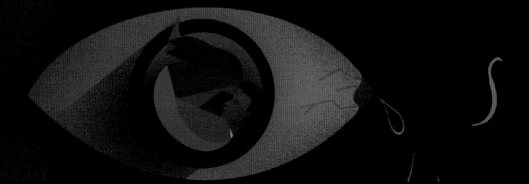

I WAS REFUSING TO EAT...

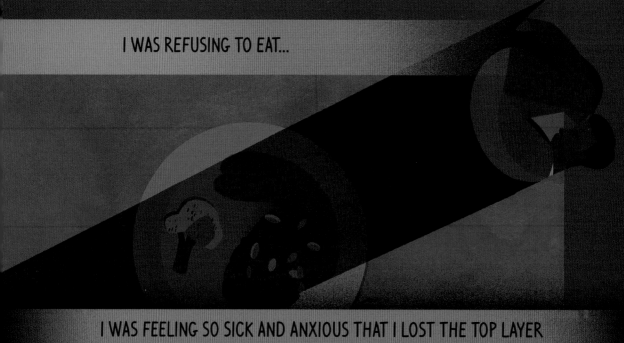

I WAS FEELING SO SICK AND ANXIOUS THAT I LOST THE TOP LAYER
OF SKIN ON MY ARMS AND MY LEGS,
BECAUSE OF THE SWEATING AND SCRATCHING.

I HAD NO SUPPORT REALLY AT THIS TIME.
THERE WAS JUST CONFUSION FROM THE PEOPLE I LIVED WITH.

MY GRANDMA HAS FIVE SISTERS
AND SIX BROTHERS.

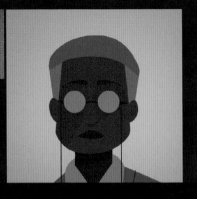

ONE OF HER SISTERS IS QUITE
MEDICALLY EDUCATED.
SHE GOT INVOLVED AND
HELD OUT A HELPING HAND.

THE FIRST TIME
SHE TRIED TO SEE ME...

I RAN OUT OF THE HOUSE –
THERE WAS JUST ABSOLUTE FEAR.

THAT NIGHT, EMERGENCY SERVICES WERE CALLED.

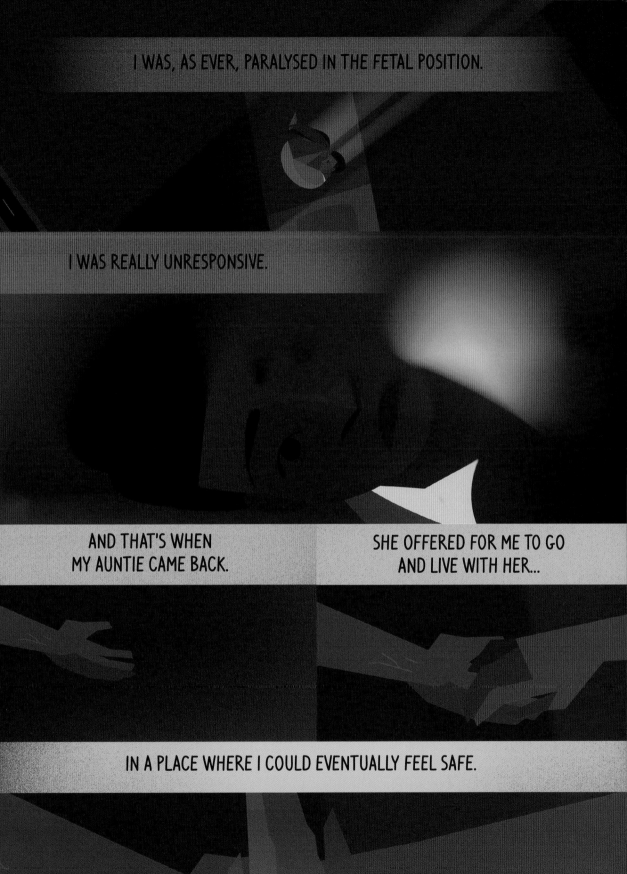

I WAS, AS EVER, PARALYSED IN THE FETAL POSITION.

I WAS REALLY UNRESPONSIVE.

AND THAT'S WHEN MY AUNTIE CAME BACK.

SHE OFFERED FOR ME TO GO AND LIVE WITH HER...

IN A PLACE WHERE I COULD EVENTUALLY FEEL SAFE.

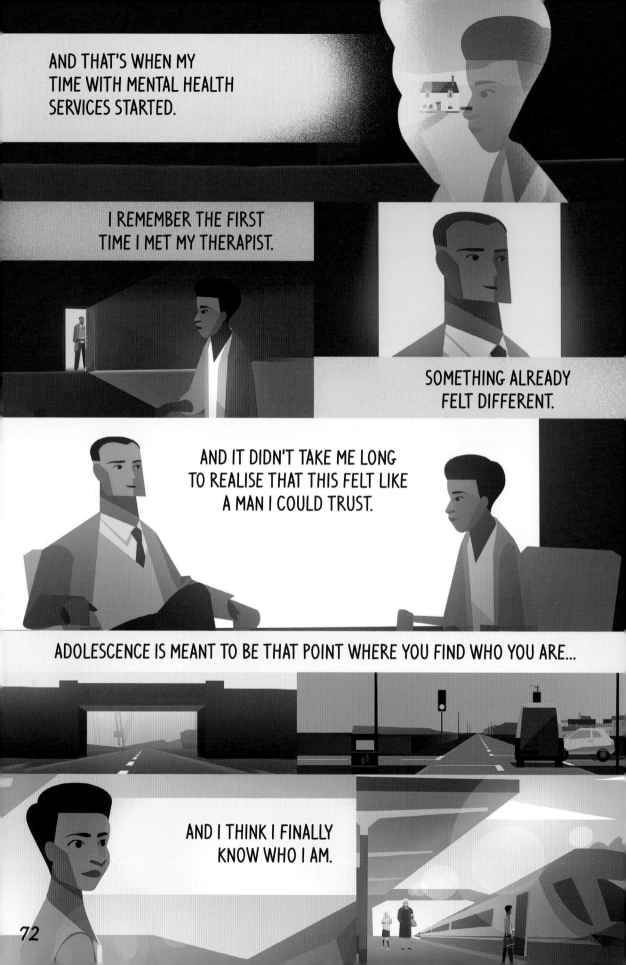

AND THAT'S WHEN MY TIME WITH MENTAL HEALTH SERVICES STARTED.

I REMEMBER THE FIRST TIME I MET MY THERAPIST.

SOMETHING ALREADY FELT DIFFERENT.

AND IT DIDN'T TAKE ME LONG TO REALISE THAT THIS FELT LIKE A MAN I COULD TRUST.

ADOLESCENCE IS MEANT TO BE THAT POINT WHERE YOU FIND WHO YOU ARE...

AND I THINK I FINALLY KNOW WHO I AM.

ELEANOR

a story about depression

MY DIFFICULTIES STARTED AROUND THE AGE OF ELEVEN, IN THE TRANSITION BETWEEN PRIMARY AND SECONDARY SCHOOL.

IT WAS A MASSIVE CHANGE FOR ME.

THE WORKLOAD...

THE CHANGE IN FRIENDSHIP GROUPS...

THE CHANGE IN
SCHOOL ENVIRONMENT...

MY ROUTINE — EVERYTHING CHANGED AT THE SAME TIME.

THAT WAS QUITE
STRESSFUL FOR ME.

I THINK THAT'S WHEN I STARTED
TO FEEL I WAS LOSING CONTROL.

I DON'T THINK
IT WAS CONSCIOUS AT FIRST...

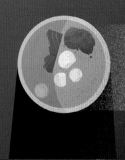

I STARTED RESTRICTING
MY FOOD INTAKE.

I THINK MY PARENTS FIRST NOTICED HOW WITHDRAWN I'D BECOME
FROM THE FAMILY, BUT ALSO MY WEIGHT LOSS.

I FELT ISOLATED FROM MY FAMILY
AND MY FRIENDS AS WELL.
MY BEHAVIOURS AND MY MOOD
WEREN'T THE SAME AS THOSE OF MY PEERS.

I DIDN'T FEEL ENJOYMENT FROM GOING TO SCHOOL
LIKE I USED TO WHEN I WAS YOUNGER.

I WASN'T GETTING OUT OF
BED MOST DAYS.

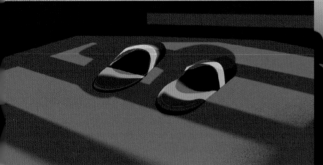

I WASN'T MAKING PLANS WITH
MY FRIENDS LIKE I USED TO.

AND ALTHOUGH I WAS ACHIEVING,
IT DIDN'T FEEL GOOD
ENOUGH ANY MORE.

I WASN'T ENJOYING THINGS
ANY MORE AND I DIDN'T
RELATE TO PEOPLE.

WHEN YOU'RE IN YOUR GLASS BOX AND IT'S ALL CLOUDED UP,
NO MATTER HOW MANY PEOPLE MIGHT BE ON THE OTHER SIDE,
YOU CAN'T SEE THEM AND YOU DON'T KNOW THEY ARE THERE ANY MORE.

THAT'S WHEN I LOST SIGHT OF THE HOPE ON THE OUTSIDE,
BECAUSE ALL I COULD SEE LOOKING BACK AT ME WAS MYSELF AND
HOW UNHAPPY I'D BECOME AND I DIDN'T SEE MYSELF EVER CHANGING.

I FELT I SHOULD BE HAPPY, THAT PEOPLE MY
AGE DIDN'T HAVE A REASON TO FEEL DEPRESSED.

BUT THERE'S NOT ALWAYS A REASON.

BEFORE I WAS AWARE OF MY MENTAL ILLNESS...

I WAS IN A GROUP OF QUITE SPORTY AND POPULAR PEOPLE.

I QUICKLY LOST THE SUPPORT OF THAT GROUP...

BECAUSE I DIDN'T FIT THEIR IDEAL
OF WHAT A PERFECT TWELVE- OR
THIRTEEN-YEAR-OLD SHOULD LOOK LIKE.

I STARTED THERAPY WITH CHILD AND ADOLESCENT
MENTAL HEALTH SERVICES. I THINK I WAS STRUGGLING
MAINLY WITH THE ISOLATION I FELT FROM MY PEERS.

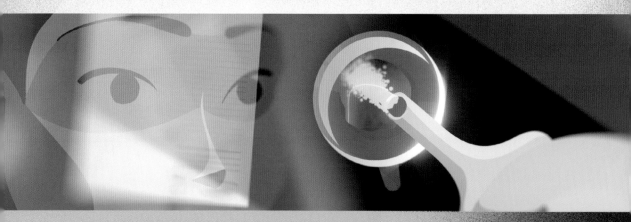

AT MY LOWEST POINT, WHEN MY SUICIDAL
THOUGHTS WERE AT THEIR WORST...

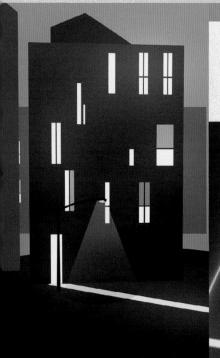

I WOULD SNEAK OUT OF MY HOUSE
WITHOUT MY PARENTS KNOWING AND
STAND AT THE SIDE OF THIS MAIN ROAD...

OFTEN WITH THE INTENTION TO REALLY INJURE
MYSELF OR EVEN KILL MYSELF, BY JUMPING
IN FRONT OF A CAR OR A MOVING VEHICLE.

SOMETIMES IF I WENT FOR A WALK...

AT MY HALF-WAY POINT WAS A BRIDGE OVER THE MAIN ROAD.

A COUPLE OF TIMES I STOOD OVER THE BARRIER...

AND WAS VERY CLOSE TO JUMPING OFF THE BRIDGE AND TRYING TO END MY LIFE.

WHEN I HIGHLIGHTED THAT TO MY THERAPIST...

I WAS ADMITTED FOR MY FIRST DEPRESSIVE-RELATED HOSPITAL ADMISSION.

WHEN I WENT BACK TO SCHOOL...

I FELT VERY CLOSELY SCRUTINISED BY A LOT OF MY TEACHERS, WHO WERE AWARE OF MY DIAGNOSIS OF MENTAL HEALTH CONDITIONS.

I FELT QUITE JUDGED BY THEM...

I FELT PUT BACK IN MY GLASS BOX.

IT WAS LIKE THEY DISREGARDED ME AND DIDN'T OFFER ME AS MUCH SUPPORT...

BECAUSE THEY DIDN'T FEEL I HAD AS MUCH POTENTIAL.

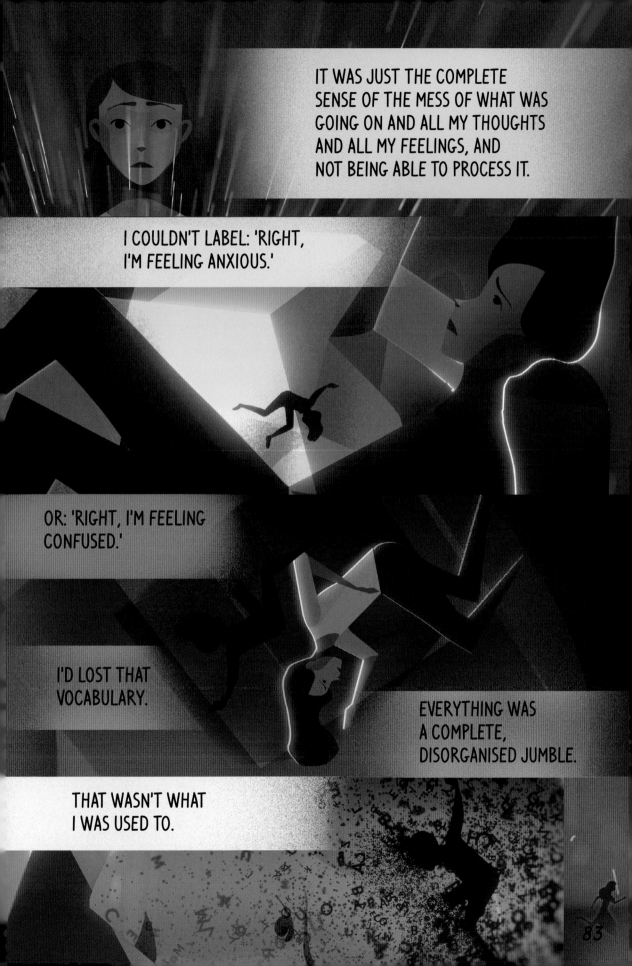

IT WAS JUST THE COMPLETE SENSE OF THE MESS OF WHAT WAS GOING ON AND ALL MY THOUGHTS AND ALL MY FEELINGS, AND NOT BEING ABLE TO PROCESS IT.

I COULDN'T LABEL: 'RIGHT, I'M FEELING ANXIOUS.'

OR: 'RIGHT, I'M FEELING CONFUSED.'

I'D LOST THAT VOCABULARY.

EVERYTHING WAS A COMPLETE, DISORGANISED JUMBLE.

THAT WASN'T WHAT I WAS USED TO.

COGNITIVE BEHAVIOURAL THERAPY WAS PROBABLY THE BEST INTERVENTION I ENGAGED WITH THROUGHOUT MY RECOVERY...

BECAUSE IT MAKES SENSE TO ME ON A LOGICAL LEVEL. IT EXPLAINS TO ME HOW MY EMOTIONS ARE LINKED WITH MY BEHAVIOURS, AND HOW THAT LINKS WITH MY THOUGHT PROCESSES.

SO SEEING THAT REALLY LOGICAL PROCESS WAS REALLY BENEFICIAL.

AND ONCE I BEGAN TO SEE LITTLE CHANGES, I SAW MYSELF MAKING BIGGER CHANGES AND THAT REALLY, REALLY HELPED ME.

SO I FEEL LIKE I'M NEARING A MUCH BRIGHTER FUTURE FOR ME AND MY MENTAL HEALTH, AND I HOPE THAT I CAN USE MY JOURNEY...

ESPECIALLY MY DARKER STAGES, TO HELP INFORM OTHERS, AS PART OF THAT BRIGHTER FUTURE.

SAM & ANEEKAH

stories about anxiety

SAM

I SPENT A LOT OF TIME ON MY OWN SO...

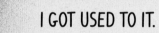

I GOT USED TO IT.

I'D JUST BE SAT THERE ON MY COMPUTER...

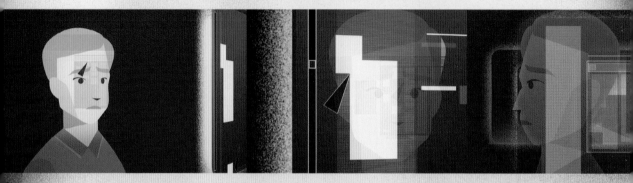

EITHER PLAYING VIDEO GAMES...

OR READING ARTICLES ONLINE.

I BECAME RATHER WITHDRAWN.

I HAD NEXT TO NO FRIENDS.

I STARTED TO GAIN ALMOST A FEAR OF PEOPLE I SUPPOSE.

ANEEKAH

I COULDN'T ARTICULATE
MY THOUGHTS VERY WELL.

I DIDN'T HAVE ANY CONFIDENCE.

I WAS VERY QUIET AND QUITE PARANOID ABOUT THE PEOPLE AROUND ME.

WHEN WE WERE PLAYING TEAM GAMES,
THEY'D PICK ME LAST.

THAT WAS AN
AWFUL EXPERIENCE.

I FELT LIKE THERE WAS SOMETHING
VERY WRONG WITH ME.

AND I COULDN'T FIGURE OUT
WHAT IT WAS.

SAM

THERE'S SO MUCH PEER PRESSURE. "OH, HAVE YOU GOT THIS NEW BAG?"

"OR THIS NEW PHONE?"

"HAVE YOU HEARD OF THIS?"

"HAVE YOU SEEN THAT?"

AND OBVIOUSLY...

I'M NOT INTO HALF THE THINGS THAT NORMAL TEENAGERS ARE INTO TODAY.

SO, I FELT THAT PRESSURE OF 'I'M A COMPLETE OUTSIDER'.

INTERACTING WITH PEOPLE WAS VERY...DIFFICULT.

I HADN'T REALLY EXPERIENCED JUST HAVING
A NORMAL CONVERSATION WITH SOMEONE.

I DIDN'T KNOW WHAT TO SAY,
I DIDN'T KNOW WHAT TO DO.

I WAS CONSTANTLY THINKING,
'DO THEY THINK I'M AN IDIOT?'

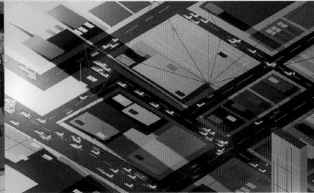

'DO THEY THINK I'M WEIRD?'

'DO THEY THINK I'M STRANGE?'
ALL SORTS OF THINGS.

ANEEKAH

WHEN I MOVED TO THE GRAMMAR SCHOOL...

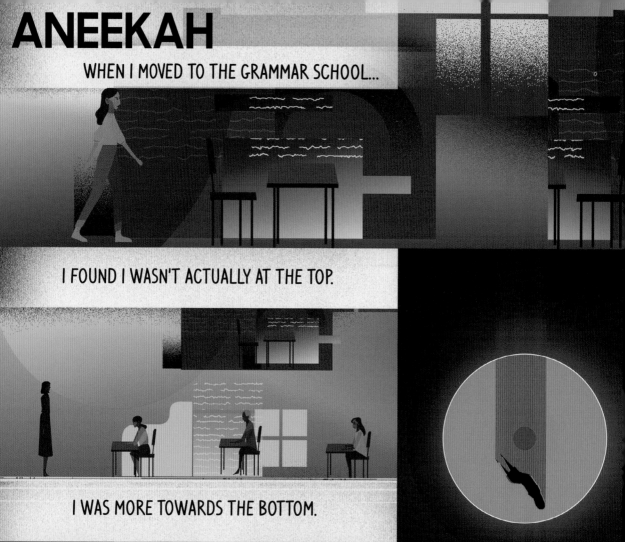

I FOUND I WASN'T ACTUALLY AT THE TOP.

I WAS MORE TOWARDS THE BOTTOM.

I WASN'T AS GOOD. OTHERS WERE MUCH BETTER
THAN ME AND IT BROUGHT ON A LOT OF ANXIETY.

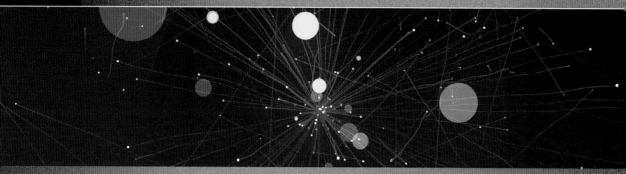

I DESCRIBED IT LIKE THE REACTIONS INSIDE THE SUN,
BECAUSE IT WAS SO INTENSE AND I DIDN'T KNOW WHAT IT WAS.

IT WAS VERY SCARY. I REMEMBER BEING WITH MY FRIENDS
AND I JUST WANTED TO ESCAPE.

I JUST WANTED TO WALK
OUT OF THE ROOM, DETACHING
MYSELF FROM THE ENVIRONMENT.
EVERYTHING WAS GOING
IN SLOW MOTION.

I WAS FINDING IT HARD
TO BREATHE SOMETIMES.

I WAS IN MY MATHS LESSON AND I WAS SITTING
IN THE MIDDLE OF TWO OR THREE PEOPLE.

I COULDN'T HEAR THE THINGS AROUND ME ANY MORE.

I JUST DIDN'T FEEL
LIKE I COULD PROCESS ANYTHING.

I WAS LOOKING DOWN AT MY PAPER,
AND LOOKING UP, AND LOOKING DOWN AGAIN.

IT WAS LIKE EVERYTHING WAS JUST QUITE FAR AWAY.

SAM

I THINK ONE OF THE TIMES THAT I FELT MOST ANXIOUS WAS IN ENGLISH CLASS.

HAVING TO STAND UP AND READ THIS BOOK...
I FELT SO ANXIOUS THAT I JUST COMPLETELY FROZE.

AND I JUST COULDN'T GET THE WORDS OUT PHYSICALLY.
LIKE THEY WERE ON THE END OF MY TONGUE, BUT THEY WERE STUCK.

SO I STOOD THERE FOR ABOUT TWO MINUTES
THEN I JUST SAT DOWN.

I WAS STUCK IN MY OWN HEAD IN THAT CLASSROOM.
I FELT SICK.

I FELT LIKE I WAS
IN A SAUNA AS WELL.
I STARTED SWEATING.

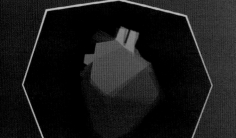

MY HEART WAS GOING
70,000 MILES AN HOUR.
IT PHYSICALLY HURT.

ANEEKAH

AT FIRST IT STARTED HAPPENING MAYBE EVERY SO OFTEN.

THEN IT STARTED INCREASING TO ONCE A WEEK...

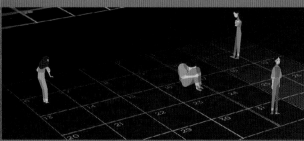

UNTIL IT GOT TO THE POINT WHERE IT WAS HAPPENING EVERY DAY.

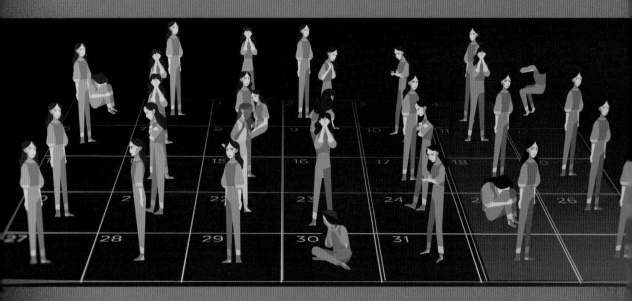

I WAS FEELING LIKE THAT ALL THE TIME.

A LOT OF PEOPLE DIDN'T BELIEVE ME,
OR THEY THOUGHT I WAS JUST 'BEING A TEENAGER'.

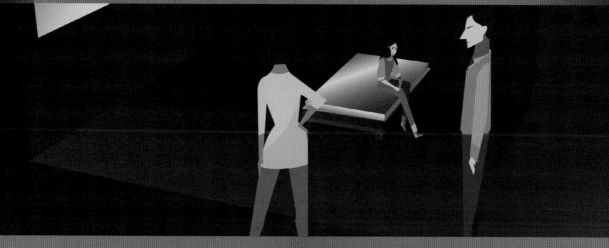

IT GOT WORSE AFTER THAT. I WITHDREW FROM MY EXAMS.

I DIDN'T DO THEM DUE TO THE
SEVERITY OF MY MENTAL HEALTH ISSUES.

SAM

SO, I JUST HAD THIS OVERWHELMING FEELING OF:
'I'M REALLY ALONE RIGHT NOW,
THIS IS ABSOLUTELY AWFUL' AND IT ALL JUST BUILT UP AND UP.

IT PHYSICALLY WOUND ME UP – I ALMOST FELT
LIKE A JACK-IN-A-BOX SOMETIMES.

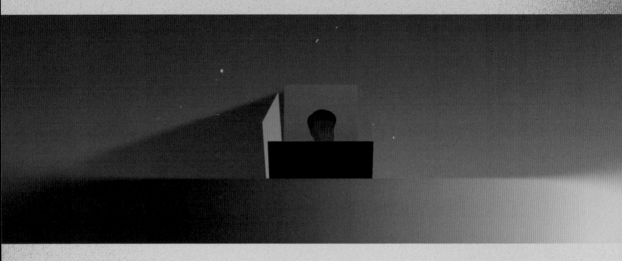

SOMEONE SLOWLY WINDING THE HANDLE UNTIL I'M JUST GOING TO POP.

ANEEKAH

AND I THOUGHT: 'I DON'T REALLY DESERVE TO LIVE,' BECAUSE,
I FELT STRESSED OUT WHEN I EVEN LOOKED AT BOOKS.

I FELT LIKE A TERRIBLE HUMAN BEING.
AND THEN I TOOK AN OVERDOSE.

I GOT FAST-TRACKED INTO ADOLESCENT
MENTAL HEALTH SERVICES

AND THEN THINGS STARTED
CHANGING FOR THE BETTER.

FIRST I SAW A KEY-WORKER WHO I THINK DID AN ASSESSMENT ON ME.

THEN I GOT TO SEE A PSYCHIATRIST.

OVER THE NEXT FEW MONTHS, I GOT TO SEE BOTH OF THEM.

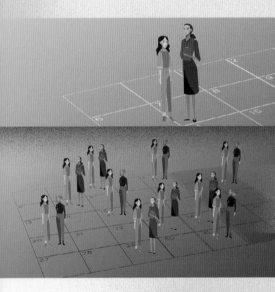

AT FIRST IT WAS WEEKLY...

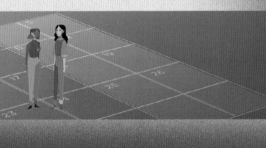

THEN IT WAS ONCE EVERY TWO WEEKS...

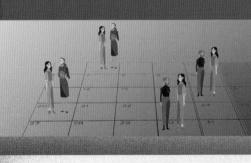

THEN IT WAS ONCE EVERY MONTH OR SO.

THAT ACTUALLY HELPED A LOT BECAUSE I FELT SUPPORTED. I FELT LIKE I COULD TALK ABOUT THINGS. LETTING THINGS OUT - YOU KNOW, JUST A RELEASE OF EMOTIONS.

PEOPLE WERE LISTENING TO ME.
I FELT LIKE I WAS ALLOWED TO BE UNWELL.

IT GOT ME TO A STATE WHERE
I COULD START DOING THINGS AGAIN...

COULD START MAKING
MY OWN CHOICES...

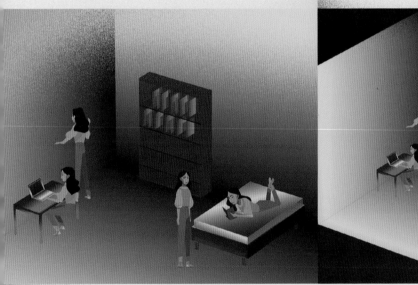

AND HELP MYSELF GET BETTER.

SAM

IT HELPED JUST TO BE ABLE TO TALK TO SOMEBODY.
I COULD SIT THERE AND TALK FOR THE HOUR.

I WAS JUST TRYING TO EXPLAIN
TO HER HOW HARD IT WAS:
"I HAVE VERY FEW FRIENDS.
I FEEL LIKE I AM NEAR ENOUGH
TERRIFIED OF PEOPLE
AND IT'S INCREDIBLY HARD."

ALL THE EMOTIONS AND ALL THE THOUGHTS
AND EVERYTHING CONSTANTLY WHIRLING AROUND.

AT SOME POINTS I JUST FELT NEAR ENOUGH PHYSICALLY DIZZY.

WHILE I WAS TALKING, THOSE NORMAL FEARS OF BEING SCARED
AND BEING WORRIED ABOUT PEOPLE...

I DIDN'T FEEL ANY OF THAT ANY MORE.

I COULD LET ALL THIS OUT BECAUSE
THERE WAS SOMEONE WHO NOT ONLY WAS
THERE, BUT WANTED TO BE THERE.

ADVISORY NOTES

SELF-HARM

Self-harm is when you hurt or damage yourself as a way of dealing with difficult feelings and experiences. In her story, India tells us how her experience of starting secondary school and the feelings it caused led her to start self-harming, and how she got help and support.

There are many reasons why someone may self-harm, like expressing feelings they're struggling with, or seeing it as something to control or a way of coping when nothing else works. If someone self-harms, that doesn't necessarily mean they want to kill themselves.

If you feel the need to self-harm, there are things you can try to let the feeling pass without hurting yourself. You could think about what has led up to you wanting to self-harm ('triggers'), and try and recognise what the urge to self-harm feels like, so you can recognise the situation or feeling in the future and do something to avoid it. You could also think of ways to distract yourself from the urge or express your emotions in a different way, such as writing letters to yourself, holding an ice cube, or doing some exercise.

If you feel you might self-harm, you can search for 'YoungMinds crisis messenger' online to talk to a counsellor, or download the Calm Harm app to help you manage the urge. Self-harming isn't safe, and if you self-harm it's important to tell a trusted adult (like a parent/carer or doctor) as soon as you can about what you're going through so they can help.

Talking to an adult you trust is an important step in getting support to stop self-harming and manage your feelings. This can also help if you're worried a friend might be self-harming. If you feel suicidal, or if you need urgent help, you or a trusted adult should call 999 as this is an emergency.

ANOREXIA

Jack's story explains how he developed a mental health problem called anorexia, also known as anorexia nervosa, and how he got help and started to recover. Anorexia is an eating disorder where you limit the food you eat to a point where you can't keep yourself healthy, often due to low self-esteem or trying to feel in control. There is a myth that only girls can be diagnosed with anorexia, but this isn't true – anyone can be affected. If you experience anorexia you may find that you are:

- Always thinking about food, your weight, or how to keep your actions secret
- Feeling worried, defensive, lonely, low, negative towards yourself, or suicidal
- Doing extra exercise or using laxatives to help get rid of what you've eaten
- Creating rules around foods you can and can't eat, counting calories, reducing how much you eat, stopping eating completely, hiding food, eating only at certain times, or weighing yourself all the time.

As a result, you may start losing weight fast, feeling tired or cold all the time, feel weak, get stomach aches or bloating or find it hard to sleep or concentrate.

If anorexia goes unmanaged for some time, you may find you start losing your hair or growing fine hair over your body, your body stops developing properly, or periods become irregular or stop.

To find out more, you can look for YoungMinds or Beat Eating Disorders online and read their information on anorexia.

Having some of these symptoms doesn't necessarily mean you have anorexia. But if you're worried about how you feel, it's best to talk to a doctor. They will be able to listen to what you're experiencing and offer you support or treatment if you need it. If you feel suicidal, or if you need urgent help, you or a trusted adult should call 999, as this is an emergency.

ADDICTION

Chloe's story describes why she first started taking drugs, and how it later led to addiction. She also explains how her addiction affected other areas of her life, how she asked her mum for help, and is now on a journey to recovery.

Addiction is a condition where it's difficult to control yourself doing something, to the point where it could cause you harm. Some common addictions include drugs, alcohol and cigarettes, and gambling. People can also get addicted to things like gaming. You might start using or doing something for any reason, like because of peer pressure, as a way of coping with something, or for fun. It can start casually but can become addictive if you develop a habit. This is when it feels so good you want to keep doing it, or if it's more unpleasant if you stop ('withdrawal') so you carry on.

Like for Chloe, addiction can affect your relationships with others and your studies. It can also affect your physical health, and your ability to deal with thoughts and feelings in a healthy way. You should talk to an adult you trust (like a parent, teacher, or doctor) if you notice yourself:

- Feeling less in control over when you do the activity or take something
- Getting withdrawal symptoms when you don't do it
- Hiding your behaviour
- Having money troubles as a result of spending money on the activity, or if you notice your mental health or wellbeing are getting worse.

To get help for addiction, a doctor may be able to talk over what you've experienced, and what treatment and support is available. Online, you can search for 'Talk to FRANK get help' for their help and advice page about drugs. You can also look for addiction information on Childline, YoungMinds and Big Deal's websites.

If you are worried about something that you have done, if you've overdosed or you're worried about a friend, this is an emergency and you should call 999 for an ambulance. If you tell them everything you can about any drugs taken, it can help save a life – and they won't tell the police.

BULLYING

In this story Ryan tells us how his bullying started, and how it negatively affected how he felt about himself and his life. He explains how he tried to cope, which wasn't working, and what happened that helped turn things around for him.

Bullying is when someone scares, ignores, teases, injures, or spreads information or rumours about someone else, to upset or hurt them on purpose. It can happen in person (at school or home), online, in games or text messages – and can even be from someone you thought was a friend or family member. Bullying can happen to anyone and is never deserved, or the fault of the person being bullied. But bullying can have a big effect, leading to low self-esteem, anxiety, depression, self-harm or anger, especially if it happens for a long time.

If you are being bullied, you can:

- Tell a trusted adult like a teacher or parent/carer, so they can help out look out for you. You can also talk to Childline confidentially if there's no one you know that you want to talk to
- Block and report the bullies, if it's online
- Try to keep a note of every time something happens, so you can use it later if you need proof, and instead of trying to remember everything
- Practise being assertive, saying 'no' and finding a pose that helps you feel confident. Kidscape's website has more ideas on how to do this.

If a friend is being bullied you can encourage them to do the above, but also offer to listen to them if they need someone to talk to, and make sure you don't support comments or social media posts that encourage the bullies. If you think you are a bully, tell an adult so they can help you. You can also stop the actions you think are hurting other people, encourage others to do the same, and apologise to those you've bullied.

DEPRESSION

Eleanor's story illustrates how her depression developed after she found changing schools difficult, and how it affected her friendships and how she thought about herself. She describes getting help from mental health services and staying in hospital, and how she had to try different treatment options before she found one that worked for her. Depression is where you feel sad, low or tearful for a long time, and stop enjoying your everyday life. Anybody can be affected by depression, and it can affect people in different ways.

Depression and low mood may be caused by going through a big change or difficult experience in your life, how you feel about yourself, or even not have a clear cause at all. Depression can affect both how you think and feel, and how you behave. You may be experiencing depression if you find you are:

- Feeling low or upset
- Feeling irritable, lonely, self-critical, or restless
- Feeling numb, tired, low energy, suicidal or wanting to self-harm
- Eating and sleeping less or more than before
- Losing interest in hobbies, watching TV, or meeting with friends.

To find out more, you can search for YoungMinds or Childline online and read their information on depression.

If you think your feelings or behaviours have changed recently and you're worried, it is best to talk to a doctor. Whether they say you have low mood or depression, they will still talk things over with you and see what treatment or support can be offered to you. If you don't want to talk to a doctor, see if there is another adult you can trust to talk to, like a parent or carer, or teacher. If you feel suicidal, have self-harmed, or feel unable to keep yourself safe, you or a trusted adult should call 999 as this is an emergency.

ANXIETY

Sam and Aneekah's stories focus on how social pressure and school grades made them gradually feel more and more anxious, and how it affected their lives - but also how getting support for their mental health then allowed them to feel what they were feeling in a safe place, feel respected, and get better.

Anxiety is where you often feel really worried, afraid or panicky, to the point where it stops you living your normal life. It comes from our natural instinct to 'fight or flight' when we're in a stressful or scary situation, and we all have times when this is normal (like before an exam or when performing in public). But it's when this instinct kicks in and we're not in a stressful situation, and we have trouble controlling the worry, that it can become a problem.

There are many different things that may cause anxiety, and it is different for everyone. Anxiety problems can affect anybody, at any stage of their life, and they can change your thoughts and feelings as well as how you behave. If you experience anxiety, you may find that you are:

- Feeling like you can't stop worrying, or worrying about the same things all the time
- Feeling tired, overwhelmed, or disconnected from yourself or the world around you
- Sweating, breathing fast, your heart's beating fast, or you're feeling faint or dizzy
- Feeling shaky, having headaches or stomachaches, needing the loo or feeling sick
- Having difficulty sleeping or eating like you were before, or having difficulty concentrating.

If you feel like your everyday life is being affected, it's best to talk to a doctor. They will listen and help find you support that will help you manage your anxiety.

There are several different types of anxiety, and you can find out more about anxiety and panic attacks by looking for YoungMinds or Childline online and reading their information.

HELPFUL WEBSITES

ANOREXIA

www.mind.org.uk/information-support/types-of-mental-health-problems/eating-problems/types-of-eating-disorders/#AnorexiaNervosa

www.beateatingdisorders.org.uk/types/anorexia

www.beateatingdisorders.org.uk/types/anorexia/signs

youngminds.org.uk/find-help/conditions/anorexia/

www.childline.org.uk/info-advice/your-feelings/eating-problems/anorexia/

SELF-HARM

www.mind.org.uk/information-support/types-of-mental-health-problems/self-harm/about-self-harm/

www.nhs.uk/conditions/self-harm/

www.childline.org.uk/info-advice/your-feelings/self-harm/self-harm/

youngminds.org.uk/find-help/feelings-and-symptoms/self-harm/

youngminds.org.uk/youngminds-professionals/our-projects/no-harm-done/

www.mind.org.uk/information-support/types-of-mental-health-problems/self-harm/helping-yourself-now

ADDICTION

www.childline.org.uk/info-advice/your-feelings/feelings-emotions/addiction/

www.childline.org.uk/info-advice/you-your-body/drugs-alcohol-smoking/drugs/

www.childline.org.uk/info-advice/you-your-body/drugs-alcohol-smoking/smoking/

digital.nhs.uk/data-and-information/publications/statistical/smoking-drinking-and-drug-use-among-young-people-in-england/2018/part-10-young-people-and-drugs-the-context

www.talktofrank.com/get-help

youngminds.org.uk/find-help/looking-after-yourself/drugs-and-alcohol/

www.nhs.uk/live-well/healthy-body/drug-addiction-getting-help/

www.mind.org.uk/information-support/guides-to-support-and-services/addiction-and-dependency/addiction-and-dependency-resources/

www.nhs.uk/live-well/healthy-body/addiction-what-is-it/

BULLYING

www.childline.org.uk/info-advice/bullying-abuse-safety/types-bullying/bullying-cyberbullying/

youngminds.org.uk/media/3557/young-minds-bullying.pdf www.kidscape.org.uk/advice/advice-for-young-people/dealing-with-bullying/

www.bullying.co.uk/advice-for-young-people/

www.anti-bullyingalliance.org.uk/sites/default/files/field/attachment/Mental-health-and-bullying-views-of-young-people-report.pdf field/attachment/Mental-health-and-bullying-views-of-young-people-report.pdf

DEPRESSION

youngminds.org.uk/find-help/conditions/depression/

www.nhs.uk/conditions/stress-anxiety-depression/low-mood-and-depression/

www.mind.org.uk/information-support/types-of-mental-health-problems/depression/about-depression/

www.mind.org.uk/information-support/for-children-and-young-people/types-of-mental-health-problems/

www.childline.org.uk/info-advice/your-feelings/feelings-emotions/depression-feeling-sad/

ANXIETY

youngminds.org.uk/find-help/conditions/anxiety/

www.childline.org.uk/info-advice/your-feelings/anxiety-stress-panic/

www.childline.org.uk/info-advice/your-feelings/anxiety-stress-panic/about-anxiety/

www.mind.org.uk/information-support/types-of-mental-health-problems/anxiety-and-panic-attacks/anxiety-disorders/

www.mind.org.uk/information-support/for-children-and-young-people/understanding-mental-health/

www.mind.org.uk/information-support/for-children-and-young-people/types-of-mental-health-problems/

www.nhs.uk/conditions/stress-anxiety-depression/understanding-panic/